"Poverty or Conservation Your National Problem"

By JAY N. "DING" DARLING
Honorary President, National Wildlife Federation

NATIONAL WILDLIFE FEDERATION
1129 VERMONT AVENUE, N. W.
WASHINGTON 5, D. C.

3 4211 000095798
DEMCO 38-297

"Poverty or Conservation Your National Problem"

By JAY N. "DING" DARLING
Honorary President, National Wildlife Federation

NATIONAL WILDLIFE FEDERATION
1129 VERMONT AVENUE, N. W.
WASHINGTON 5, D. C.

Fifth Printing
Single copies $.25 each
Ten or more copies $.10 each

INTRODUCTION

The National Wildlife Federation is happy to present to you this article by Jay N. "Ding" Darling, told in the way that only he can tell it. We hope that you will read it carefully and give serious thought to the problems it unfolds. These are your problems, affecting you and your way of life, and the future of your children.

This article has not been prepared for the purposes of entertainment. It is information that is being passed on to you with the earnest hope that since you have an important stake in the social and economic future of America, you will take an active part in the promotion of sound programs of conservation and restoration of our natural resources.

Your cooperation is solicited, and your comments and suggestions as well.

"Poverty or Conservation Your National Problem"

By JAY N. "DING" DARLING
Honorary President, National Wildlife Federation

Any nation is rich so long as its supply of resources is greater than the needs of its people. After that no nation is self-supporting. Somewhere between those two extremes lies America and its problem of a world free from want.

Since it seems practically decided that America is going to have company for dinner, it might be a good idea to have a look at our pantry shelves and count our food coupons. Any good housewife would do as much.

Feeding the war-starved world with the surpluses produced in a land of free men under Democratic Government would seem a reasonable method by which to create a favorable impression on the people who have starved under Fascism.

At any rate, the invitations are out and the hungry guests are arriving: India, China, Greece, Algeria, Tunisia, a portion of Russia, some of England, a little of Spain, Sicily, Southern Italy, and presumably all the rest of Europe as fast as portions of it are liberated, to say nothing of helping to feed the armies of our Allies.

It is a large order, but our agriculturists have reached a new record peak of production. Technological advancements have greatly increased the crop yields, and victory gardens—in spite of the bean bugs, blisters and amateur efforts—have filled the new horn of plenty from a hitherto undeveloped source of food supply. Admittedly many thousands of acres still remain idle, or through neglect fall far below their maximum production. An International Food Conference has pooled the estimated resources of the world and made out a menu, which they declare holds promise of nutrition for all. We are proceeding to set the table on that assumption. Our objective is a world free from want, and for an unspecified length of time, at least, a large part of the food supplies are to be furnished by America.

Facing the Facts

Surely there is no one who would wish to destroy that fine hope and laudable intention, but it might as well be admitted that feeding the hitherto undernourished world cannot be accomplished simply by all joining hands and singing "God Bless America." It is going to demand some very serious thinking and even more serious doing. What must be done we must do in the interest of a better world of which we are an inseparable part. Such sacrifices as we may be called upon to make cannot possibly equal the cost of wars and the threat of future wars. If the free nations of the world will join in a cooperative union to accomplish that objective our contribution may be costly but compared to the wastage of war it will be cheap and may be set down as money and resources well spent.

So much for the compulsory needs now confronting us. If that is the price of world peace we must pay it. But what is the use of thus saving our precious lives if we are going to commit national suicide by wasting our resources faster than we eat them? **For instance, while we are thinking about how we are going to feed the undernourished world there is more beefsteak and potatoes, roast duck, ham and eggs, and bread and butter with jam on it being washed down our rivers each year in the form of good rich topsoil than all the food we export to our Allies and distressed populations in any current year.** That is a lot of groceries. It may look like nothing but mud to you as it swirls down our silt-laden streams, but it is the very substance out of which our magnificent crops are produced. It is the cream off the top of our continent.

The Loss of a Capital Investment

That tremendous loss by unchecked soil erosion has been going on for years and still continues in spite of all the noise and shouting about soil conservation. Even a Democratic form of government, with all its blessings, cannot replace lost topsoil. Only Mother Nature can do that, and it takes centuries of precious time.

If an alien aggressor attempts to steal so much as a square inch of our sacred land the whole nation rushes to arms, but there are twenty-five million cubic feet of our richest land washing away each year—lost forever—and no one, well almost no one, gives it a thought. Peculiar, isn't it? But no more astonishing than the complete disregard with which the people of this nation have watched their forests, well stocked lakes, streams and other natural resources disappear with unparalleled rapidity. That is a simplified way of saying that while we are worrying our silly heads over our food ration coupons, we are allowing the substance of our human paradise to slip through our fingers without protest.

The trail of civilization is strewn with the wrecks of derelict races and nations which fell by the wayside when their natural resources played out. By the way, did you know that the fabled land of Canaan, once flowing with milk and honey, is now a desert? Canaan is now on relief and we are furnishing it. How and why a land once flowing with milk and honey should be reduced to starvation and rags is a fair object for study; and how to avoid it the lesson which conservationists try to teach. The mystery is that so few people should care to learn it.

As long as we in America could pick up the telephone and get anything we wanted delivered to our door for the asking—whether it was fresh strawberries in midwinter ripened in Texas sunshine or two-inch sirloin steaks from cornfed beef—it seemed almost impossible to get the people of the United States to think there was any limit to our natural resources or to take seriously the subject of guarding against rapid depletion. Since we seemed to have plenty of everything why worry about it? Were we not the richest country in the world? Then, why all this bother about conservation?

The Warning—Disregarded

Until this last war we thought we had so much of everything that our resources would last forever. Within one short year, we have tumbled from this dreamy height in the clouds and landed, none too comfortably, in a bramble bush of painful shortages, which has scratched and jabbed us in a lot of places we never even suspected had feelings.

When Japan moved into Manchuria ten years ago, we still closed our eyes and ears to the open threat to our safety. The majority of our people would not take this war seriously either until the attack on Pearl Harbor.

We realize now we were actually warned of the war that was to come, and the warnings to this nation that the depletion of our natural resources has already reached the danger point are written just as plainly across the face of this continent as were the threats made by Hitler, Mussolini and Hirohito. They are written in million-acre patches of *denuded forests, abandoned farms, dust bowls* and *dried-up rivers, springs* and *lakes.* Tens of thousands of so-called "Okies," refuges from wrecked land, have paraded back and forth before our eyes on the public highways crying for relief within the last decade. The portent of these warnings has been interpreted and shouted from the housetops by the prophets of conservation, but the public turned a deaf ear. We blamed our economic breakdown on Wall Street, on Herbert Hoover, the Republican Party, on Capitalism, on Industry. We blamed it on most anything except on depleted natural resources. To name the real cause would reflect on our own intelligence and scandalous waste of which every one of us in this country is more or less guilty. As a remedy we brought forth a great number of patent medicine tonics. We tried to spend ourselves rich. Redistribution of wealth and the forty-hour week were recommended as cure-alls. Made-work projects and plowing under surplus crops were applied liberally. There is no attempt to deny or affirm the minor virtues which were claimed for these various specifics, but none of them touched the seat of the disease, which lay, at least in part, in the rapidly shrinking agricultural lands, the denudation of rich forest areas, the pollution and overfishing of our lakes, streams and coastal areas, and the overgrazing of our western grasslands. The patent medicines had cost us forty billion dollars, but the major problem of checking the disease of dwindling resources had scarcely been touched. Then came the war. The new emergency put upon our natural resources the greatest burden that had ever been known. That burden will continue until long after the signing of peace. While the war-torn world is healing its wounds a large proportion of the sustenance will continue to come from our continent. That again raises the question of how long we can continue to *feed more and more people on less and less productive soil.* That we are going to have to feed more and more people is a foregone conclusion. The only other alternative is to materially remedy the *"less and less"* soil situation by known methods of soil management and the application of scientific conservation principles. Since it is obvious that *more and more people* cannot live on *less and less,* forever and ever, world without end, we should face the problem frankly and either apply conservation seriously or resign ourselves to the inevitable consequences of a *greatly lowered standard of living.*

We Will Win the War Against Our Foreign Enemies

It took Pearl Harbor to awaken us to the dangers of a three-year-old war which threatened our Democratic way of life. With courage, determination and sacrifice of blood and national treasure we recovered from that blow and won the war against our human enemies but if we do not take warning and defend our natural resources from this headlong race of waste and depletion we will lose a battle from which our continent never will recover. The road back from Pearl Harbor was short and easy compared to the road back from a continent shorn of its natural resources. The Prodigal Son was lucky. He went back home to the fatted calf after he had squandered his all in riotous living. When we have spent our heritage of natural resources in riotous living there won't be any fatted calf or sympathetic father to go back to. Mother Nature is unforgiving. When we have spent our natural resources, we have spent everything, and we are jolly well doing just that right now.

It seems strange that we are not more concerned over this inevitable prospect, especially in this day of horrors when we see the cumulative results of world-wide surplus populations seeking to extricate themselves from the pinch of worn-out soils and shrunken resources by wholesale indulgence in mass murder and international burglary. Whatever the pretexts may be by which Japan, Italy and Germany attempt to justify the slaughter of their neighbors and the seizure of their territory, the undisputed facts are plain that Japan could no longer sustain her bulging population on the decreasing resources within her island boundaries. Italy had to have expansion of both territory and food supplies or suffer ever-increasing national poverty.

Germany must have land, food and a place to send her surplus of people or accept a gradual decline in living standards and face eventual national disintegration. Each tried to supply her own needs by forcibly taking them from the neighbors.

Germans, Italians and Japanese learned by sad experience that a loaf, however large, can be cut into only so many slices. With all due reverence to the parables of Holy Writ, mere man has found no way to feed an ever-increasing multitude with fewer and fewer loaves and fishes.

Will We Win Our War for Conservation?

That is the lesson which conservationists are trying to drive home to the people of this continent before it is too late. The rich topsoils, the sparkling waters and rich growth of vegetation, together with its minerals and wildlife, which made this continent the richest prize in the history of civilization are **not inexhaustible**, in spite of our common habit of thinking so. If intelligently cared for they can be made to last indefinitely and produce abundantly. But if any one of the three is depleted by wasteful practices and slothful mismanagement our American continent will be broken out with a rash which no sociological salve can cure. Then America will not only be unable to *"feed the world"* but by its own standards of living will be unable to feed itself. When that day comes, if it is not here already, *economic depressions, revolutionary uprisings* and *internal discontent* will follow as night follows day, just as these same symptoms have marked the decline of every center of civilization since the beginning of history. Many of the tragedies which have come upon portions of our population during the recent heart-breaking years of depression were the direct results of disregard or ignorance of the simplest conservation principles. In spite of all technological discoveries those same tragedies will be surely multiplied as we take on additional responsibilities resulting from the war.

Productivity of soil is the *"bottle-neck"* of human existence. It has been so since man's sojourn on earth began.

History is one continuous succession of migrations from exhausted soil to new fertile fields which nature has spent millions of years in creating. There is only one formula for production of fertile soil and man has no part in that creative process. All he can do is use it and make it last as long as possible.

How Nature Works

Chlorophyl, that green pigment in vegetation, plus sunshine, has laid down all the topsoil, all the coal, all the oil and every organic living thing on which mankind has subsisted and must subsist forever. For chlorophyl is that magic green element in vegetation which alone can capture the carbon dioxide from the atmosphere and combine it with hydrogen to make all the carbohydrates which enrich the soil and keep us alive. Without countless centuries of chlorophyl and sunshine cooperation we could have no food, no fire, no crops, no life, nothing. When we inherited this continent we fell heir to a *hundred-million* years of cumulative transformation of raw volcanic rock to rich loam, grassy plains, primeval forests, a myriad population of fur-bearing animals and waters teeming with fish and aquatic life—all the product of the chlorophyl factory. Don't forget that when this rich endowment is gone its only replenishment must come through that same *small bottle-neck* of *chlorophyl plus sunshine.*

Can any thoughtful person say that with 80% of our forests already cut down, 75% of our grasslands grazed to a stubble and millions of acres of underbrush cleared from our hillsides that we have not constricted the bottle-neck instead of enlarging it?

Those who cite surpluses of grain and cotton to contradict the threat of shortages are only looking through the keyhole at a nation-wide, yes world-wide, problem. Those surpluses were produced at heavy cost to the richest remaining topsoil areas in America. Robbing the rich soils to produce larger and larger annual harvests may be the most costly type of farming practiced. It was exactly that type of farming which started millions of acres of American farm land down the road to the desert.

The Human Angle

The threatened approach of shortages in natural resources is not announced by headlines in the daily press. Any editor of a local paper would be hung from the nearest apple tree who dared warn prospective citizens to stay away because the home town and its environs was on its last legs due to exhausted resources. Such embarrassing information is carefully concealed from the world by local Chambers of Commerce, Real Estate Dealers' Associations and Retail Merchants. Can you imagine railroads advising summer tourists not to buy tickets to the Minnesota lake districts because nine-tenths of their lakes have lost their once prolific fish and game populations? No land boomer was ever known to tell a prospective purchaser that the three former owners went broke trying to make a living on the ranch he was trying to sell to the fourth. Nor would an Arizona silver mine broker reveal that the precious metals had all been taken out of the mine by its previous operator, any more than a second-hand auto dealer would tell a customer that the bearings were burned out, the battery dead and the transmission gears stripped on a car he was offering for sale. Florida does not advertise that it costs more for the fertilizer to raise oranges in that state than you can get for the ripened fruit and Iowa is careful not to let anyone know that the southern third of its farm land has been so badly eroded that whole counties have gone on relief and that their schools, churches and local governments are bankrupt. The U. S. Reclamation Service does not publicize the number of irrigation projects which have cost the taxpayers millions and then wrecked the family fortunes of the settlers who tried to farm the irrigated lands. The National Forest Service does its best to arouse the public to the dangers of forest fires but it does not emphasize the fact that forest fires are taking toll of our American forests faster than Nature, with the assistance of the U. S. Forest Service and all the state forest departments, can grow them. And so on and so forth ad infinitum. Thus it happens that the people of this country have remained in ignorance of the progress and depth of depletion which has pulled from under them the sustaining foundation of their prosperity.

As a nation we did not concern ourselves over what was to become of the army of lumberjacks, sawmill operators, the local storekeepers, school teachers and village inhabitants when the great primeval forests of Michigan, Wisconsin and Minnesota were all finally harvested and cut into lumber. Even less conscious were we of the fate of the thousands of families of the once prosperous fishing villages on the southern shores of Lake Erie when suddenly the prolific runs of fresh water herring gave out and fishermen, boatmakers, net-weavers and associated industries were left without any means of livelihood. Ghost towns that were once thriving fishing villages line the coastal waters of the Atlantic, the Pacific, the Great Lakes and our major rivers—each one a tombstone to dead resources.

Social and Economic Factors

''Abandoned farm'' is a familiar term which has fallen upon our ears and slid off with no more effect than a drop of water on a duck's back, but a single abandoned farm is sodden with tragedy and suffering for the members of the little family who could not make a living on it and had to abandon all hope there. Multiply that tragedy by a million abandoned farms (there are many more than a million abandoned farms in this country already) and that term ''abandoned farm'' assumes a foreboding significance which we as a nation have ignored.

Need we mention more examples in order to be convincing? It could be done until every nook and cranny of our continent had been shown to be the victim of similar circumstances. Each in its turn inflicted no stunning blow to our national economy but the cumulative effect of all of them together has built up a total of profound significance. The early symptoms are as insidious in their approach as a creeping paralysis whose earlier effects are only inconvenient but which finally paralyze the whole body. By the same token, the day when everyone in the United States will go comprehensively hungry is a long way off but the widening margin of our population who do go underfed because of disappearing forests, land and water is gaining new recruits by the hundreds of thousands annually. The climax of exhausted resources will be violent and without mercy. Once that climax is reached the restoration is as slow as the ages of Nature.

We know now that much of the rapid exhaustion which has taken place in America was entirely unnecessary, due largely to ignorance and wasteful practices which could have been avoided without loss to current profits. If we begin now the intelligent application of those same principles which might have prevented the past waste we can at least insure continuity of use of what we have left. We possibly can accomplish a restoration of some of that which has been lost. It is the application of such principles and practices which, grouped together, is called "Conservation."

Conservation is an organized campaign to eliminate the *"bottle-neck"* in the economic mechanism for national welfare and if it can't eliminate the bottle-neck at least it can keep it from growing smaller and choking us to death.

The Laws of Nature

Conservation is not just a sentimental hobby nor a fanciful hope of idle dreamers, of duck hunters, of fishermen or bird lovers. Conservation is a science whose principles are written in the oldest legal code in the world—The Laws of Nature. It has taken the scientists longer to discover and interpret those laws than it has taken the archaeologists to unearth the story of the Egyptian Pyramids and King Tut. In spite of their greater significance to man, King Tut gets all the publicity and more people know about King Tut and his unearthed treasure than know why the region where he lived is now desert. The latter item of information is, however, much the more important of the two.

Ignorance of the laws of Nature has been, and still is, more responsible for the infractions than willful malpractice. It is therefore necessary before any real progress towards conservation can take place that the educational fraternity shoulder a large part of the responsible burden. It is obviously hopeless to divert our mass population from their ingrown destructive habits when they are not aware of either the natural laws or the dire consequences of their violation.

A Challenge to Education

How the educational institutions shall accomplish this task is for professional educators to determine. Suffice it here to say that the job must be done and done soon. It is the job of scientists to interpret and correlate the natural laws in such form that the educators may make them clear to the oncoming generations. In a large measure the natural scientists are far ahead of the educators with their work. For instance, scientific research has determined by experiment and proved by demonstration that plants have vital influence on moisture in the soil, one of the most important relationships in human welfare. But Botany teachers still occupy the minds of their pupils with identification of species and grade the students accordingly, while geologists, although water is the most precious element within their sphere, ignore it altogether and drill their classes on the relative hardness of horn-blends and talc, and how to distinguish fluorite from feldspar by the number of facets to their crystals. Biologists, whose province is the teaching of the interrelationship of all living things, have wandered off into that rarefied atmosphere which surrounds the eternal mystery of when and how life enters protoplasm. Yet within the natural laws of these common school studies lie the secrets of *droughts, floods* and *dust bowls, eroded topsoil, deserts* and DESTITUTION.

Why are so many of our fresh water springs, once perpetually flowing, now dry?

Why do rivers which within our memory once flowed bank full the year round now dwindle to nothing in midsummer?

What man-created influences have caused a continuous and rapid falling of the subsoil water table of our continent?

What happened to Nature's balance in the great stretches of western grasslands which has made them barren deserts and the ranch houses vacant?

How long will it take to replace the nine inches of rich topsoil which have washed off the farms of the Mississippi Valley? How?

What essential function to life do green leaves perform without which no human being could exist?

What is the source of all sugar, starch, fat, coal and oils and is there any substitute method of production which men can provide?

Why are there no more salmon in the Atlantic Coast rivers of the United States of America?

Why do lakes which once had crystal waters and an abundance of aquatic economic resources now grow green scum and no fish?

What has become of the millions of people who once lived on the now denuded forests, abandoned farm land and exhausted fishing waters?

The answers to all these and many more questions like them are now written so that anyone who cares to may read in the simple language of the natural research scientists. And the fate of our future generations rests upon their application to everyday living.

Research scientists have gone a long way to provide the formulas by which Conservation can be accomplished. The public, hydraulic and sanitary engineers, industrialists and, alas, educators, have been slow to apply or even think of these vital essentials to man's existence while our population grows larger and our productive resources shrink.

Selfish Interests Responsible

Local Chambers of Commerce and Congressmen still rush the doors of the Treasury for millions to build dams which will produce $25,000.00 worth of electricity a year but destroy nine million dollars' worth of natural income and throw thousands out of employment. It has been done recently.

A slaughter-house or a paper mill may employ 100 men and increase the local bank clearings to the gratification of the city fathers but at the same time destroy the livelihood of 500 families downstream through pollution of the once productive waters.

"Reclamation projects" may (and have done so time without number) spend tremendous sums for irrigation and find that they have robbed Peter of a fortune to pay Paul a pittance.

Such hastily promoted projects, instigated for quick profit and exploitation, are seldom preceded by even a gesture of scientific investigation to determine in advance what the consequences may be to the people of the country as a whole. Because the simple principles of Nature's laws are not a part of the average man's learning, there is no one to protest. What is even more lamentable, the average understanding is so low that they do not even know they are being hurt until the sledge hammer falls. Congressmen, army engineers, most Governors, state legislators and all known Mayors and County Supervisors are as oblivious to the import of Conservation principles as Adolf Hitler is to truth and human justice. That makes it almost unanimous, and yet the fundamentals are as easy to understand as the fact that long grass will gather and hold more snowflakes than short grass and hence provide more moisture in the soil for the next season's crops.

I could tell you of an experimental area of 35,000 acres of land which ten years ago had not a spear of grass visible, wherein seven flowing springs had gone permanently dry and life was practically extinct. That same 35,000 acres is now knee high with lush vegetation, the seven springholes are again full of water the year 'round and a thousand head of cattle could be fed without over-grazing. It didn't take any fertilizer. It didn't take any 25-million-dollar irrigation project to restore it to production. Only an application of the simplest principles of conservation management.

The obvious and simple practicability of Nature's methods turn out to be man's best aids. It did take scientists—and good ones—working diligently over a period of many years, to provide the proof that the principles of conservation would work, and why. It is too much to claim that the subject has been scientifically exhausted. It hasn't, but a great deal more is known than is being taught or applied, and the scientific research is a long way ahead of the procession.

Let us see if we can outline a few conclusions which will fix in mind the objectives of conservation and the processes which are essential to its accomplishment:

1. **No nation can permanently endure which consumes its natural resources faster than Nature, with scientific aids, can replace them.**
2. **Conservation is the science of greatest possible production without diminishing the source materials.**
3. **Conservation seeks by the application of the natural laws to provide methods by which perpetual production may be substituted for destructive exploitation.**
4. **Conservation is the exponent and advocate of careful scientific study and diagnosis before major operations are performed on our basic economic mechanism.**
5. **It is essential that whenever Nature's productive balance is invaded that adequate replacements or equivalent substitutions be provided as insurance against diminishing returns.**
6. **It is a primary requisite of conservation that no project which makes use of natural resources is justified whose costs to the people of this nation are greater than the local profits.**

All these seemingly axiomatic precepts are, as a matter of fact, just another way of saying that you can't feed and clothe more and more people on less and less productive resources. The repetition of this axiomatic fact is intentional. To the newcomers who approach these more serious aspects of conservation for the first time, the emphasis on food production to the neglect of mineral resources may cause some questioning which should be answered here.

Organic and Inorganic Resources

Resources by Nature are divided into two classifications: those which are renewable by human efforts and those which by Nature are not renewable. In a measure, all organic resources are renewable. Forests can be replaced by reforestation; grasses and surface vegetation if destroyed can be replanted. Furs of wild animals can be replaced by wool from domestic animals or textiles made from vegetable matter. Depleted animal life can be renewed by scientific breeding and restocking. Even soil depletion can be, in a measure, renewed under advantageous conditions by prescribed vegetation management.

On the other hand, the mines which produce our inorganic or mineral resources such as silver, aluminum, iron, tin, zinc and kindred elements cannot be restocked. They are therefore classed as non-renewable resources. There are, to be sure, dangers which threaten serious inconvenience if by mismanagement and waste our stocks of essential minerals run short, but these hazards concern industrial production rather than the essentials to sustain life.

I venture to say that no one would like to contemplate living in this modern world without the conveniences provided through industrial production. If that is bad, think how much worse it would be to live in a world from which the supply of food, fuel and clothing had been exhausted. Hence the emphasis on "renewable" resources, for if you do not "renew" your "renewable" resources you won't have any use for the "non-renewable" anyway. King Midas found that out when everything he touched turned to gold and he could not eat.

What Science Can Do

Considering the almost unlimited possibilities for substitutions in the field of minerals and inorganic, unrenewable materials, we can say with considerable degree of confidence that there will be no "bottle-neck" in the long run of metals for industrial needs and human requirements, at least in times of peace.

It is unfortunate, however, that in the process of producing substitutes for metallic materials, an extra strain is put upon the organic sources of materials, where the real bottleneck is located.

Running through the whole scale of new plastic materials: Rayon, Nylon, Lucite, Pliofilm and the Bakelite group, to mention only a few, the constituent elements are chiefly of organic origin and every known organic substance, living or dead, has come and must continue to come through that single agency of green leaf chlorophyl plus sunshine. If there were any virtue in wishing, we could wish that our alchemists would pick on something besides carbon to transmute into mineral substances. Everybody wants to use carbon for something or other and no one has ever been able to make any.

In the field of heat, energy and power production, there is no fuel which is not of organic origin, with the possible exception of mineral oil, whose mysterious origin has not been satisfactorily proved. Both coal and oil must be classed among the non-renewable resources and any substitutions must come from the organic or vegetable family. Synthetic gasoline, the alcohols and all combustibles are made from organic matter. Then add further to the strain on the organic bottle-neck all the foods we eat (whether animal or vegetable) all the textiles, linen, cotton or wool, all the millions of tons of paper used daily, all the gunpowder, cigarettes and feathers on women's hats. To put all expended energy also in the list would involve some duplication but its drain upon organic resources is so vast a daily item that it should not be neglected in the comprehensive concept. From the tiniest flip of a fish's tail to the throbbing engines of the largest steam turbine in the world, every move burns up, directly or indirectly, some of the organic matter laboriously produced by the minute green cells in leaves.

What Only Nature Can Do

Picture then in your mind, if you will, this vast army of human demands lined up like a breadline before a soup kitchen and waiting to be served by that sole producer of relief rations, the green pigment in vegetation, and you will get a new conception of what a "bottle-neck" means. There is no other source. Without green vegetation there is no chlorophyl. Without soil and water there is no vegetation. Every grassy plain or forest denuded of its vegetation and every marsh drained of its water by man's wasteful practices constricts the bottle-neck. Every careless farmer who by negligence allows the topsoil to wash from his land shortens the period of time that his soil can contribute to human needs.

Among modern current events I can think of no more excruciating mental agony than must have been suffered by those battered troops on Bataan Peninsula, scanning the skies to the east in vain for the relief planes which never were to arrive. That is very real to all of us, and tragic in our total helplessness to aid. I wish it were possible to dramatize for you the utter hopelessness of our situation on the North American continent when through failure to heed conservation warnings the pinch of organic shortages overtakes us all and from which no relief will be immediately available.

There was a time when population pressures on this continent were easily relieved by opening up new lands. Today there are no new frontiers. We must sit down where we are and plan our subsistence for the next ten thousand years on what we have left of our organic resources.

Today we are all busy with war. Everyone is employed, or should be. But tomorrow when the war is over we will be again confronted with the problem of peace-time employment. The trials of the late depression are too recent not to be remembered. But no one seemed to take seriously the fact that our population had increased by leaps and bounds while our soils, grasslands, wildlife and forests had shrunk by at least ninety million acres within the last decade.

Did you ever play "Going to Jerusalem" or "Musical Chairs" where the guests at a party march to music around a double row of chairs which contians fewer seats than there are guests? When the music stops everyone tries to sit down. Because there are fewer seats than there are players somebody generally sprawls on the floor or is left standing without any chair. Then another chair is removed, the music and marching start again and so on until there is but one chair left.

One hundred thirty million people in our country have been playing the same game only we have been using land instead of chairs and an amazing number of people already have no place to sit down. Then, if we add the distressed populations of Europe who must be fed, our little game becomes serious business indeed because the exploitation of resources for war in the interest of national survival has exceeded any peace-time exploitation we have ever known. When the emergency is past there will be new bald spots on the surface of our continent where natural resources have been exhausted. Those bald spots will spell less food and more homeless men.

In our desperation, if we follow our customary pattern we will juggle the currency, reduce working hours and redistribute wealth, we may even try substituting Dictatorship for Democracy, but none of them nor all of them put together will restore the soils we have so wastefully depleted. Such inventions of the sociologists and economic doctors will be of no avail in reforesting our cut-over timberlands. They cannot reclothe the Dust Bowls with grass by social reform, neither can they bring back the eroded topsoil from the Mississippi Delta and put it on the abandoned farms. Once exhausted, there is no simple cure. Only a public aroused to the dangers can provide the prevention before it is too late.

Conservation becomes, then, not a matter of sentimental appreciation of the beauties of Nature. Neither is it an idle humor of cloistered scientists in their experimental laboratories. It is grim business for statement and government executives and we wont have statement and executives who will know what it is all about until the teaching fraternity takes over the job of educating a new crop.

Conservation and History

Some day a new historian will arise who will revolutionize our study of the past and give us a much better understanding of the problems which we ourselves are meeting. This new history will give us an interpretation of the causes which produced the events, rather than a compilation of dynasties, dates and victorious generals. Instead of telling us in detail *how* Genghis Khan and Alexander the Great fought their battles, the new historian will tell us *why* they fought their wars of conquest. And the reasons will exactly parallel the causes which led the Japanese to invade the Asiatic continent, the Italians to slaughter the Ethiopians and Hitler to shatter all the international covenants to loot Europe. From the first racial conflicts of written history on down to the present day, wars have sprung from the same background: an increased racial population wore out its natural resources and relieved the pressure within by arming its surplus men and moving in on the less depleted pastures of its neighbors.

Archaeologists tell us that this process started in the Gobi Desert and whether or not that was the cradle of the human race, the fossilized remnants of profuse vegetation and abundant animal life are all that remain to show that man once lived there in obvious abundance until depleted natural resources forced the inhabitants to seek new lands. Out of this area came successive waves of migrations which moved westward into Mongolia, India, Persia, Arabia, Turkestan, Palestine, Mesopotamia, the Nile and the Sahara, the Caucasus, the Mediterranean state and finally into what we now call continental Europe.

Buried in the dust and rubble of ages along these ancient migration lanes are crumbling palaces of kings and buried cities which once housed thriving populations, convincing evidence that those desert lands were once sufficiently productive to maintain prosperous communities. You couldn't pasture a healthy Dakota grasshopper there now on 100 square miles. Fabled lands "flowing with milk and honey," the valleys of the Ganges and Euphrates, Arabia, Persia and Babylon were not always the deserted wastes they are today, inhabited only by struggling remnants of the former hordes searching an exhausted land for sustenance for their flocks and a meager livelihood for themselves. Architects and artisans do not go off into a desert to erect such majestic designs to masonry as mark the remains of Bagdad.

What vast natural resources must have blossomed on the sandy wastes of Egypt to support the armies employed to build the Pyramids! For every stone in their vast bulk there must have been at least a hundred acres of land in full and continuous production to feed the laborers who quarried the rock and hoisted it into place. Let your imagination fill the gap between the vast operations during the building of the temples of Karnak and this flea-bitten remnant of Egypt which dips from the Nile enough water to raise a handful of rice, the per diem ration of its remaining population.

Few know that the mysterious city of Timbukto, a ghost town of prehistoric origin isolated by miles of arid waste in the middle of the Sahara Desert, was once surrounded by fertile fields and olive groves. Buried beneath its desert sands is complete evidence that Africa's great "dust bowl" once was as rich as the Mississippi Valley. Giant primitive forests, lakes and rivers once spread across the vast wastes of the Sahara.

Between the Gobi Desert and Mesopotamia, a thousand Genghis Khans, Attilas and Nebuchaadnezzars fought for the riches which these ancient lands once produced. They wouldn't be worth fighting for now if it were not for the oil deposits (of which the ancients had no knowledge) hidden deep beneath the earth's crust. And speaking of Dakota grasshoppers, as I was a moment ago, is a reminder that grasshopper plagues and human migrations, like "the Colonel's lady and Judy O'Grady," are sisters under the skin. Both come about through populations expanded beyond the tolerance of the food supply and when they migrate both seek a new location where vegetation is rich and plentiful. Both leave desolation in their wake and when they have exhausted the food supply of their latest invasion they move on to another. It takes no imagination on the part of anyone who has ever seen a grain field after the grasshoppers have finished it to see there the replica of man's migration path down through the ages.

Is it just a coincidence that those once rich lands where civilization has lived the longest are all now deserts and unable to support a one-thousandth part of their former populations, or is there a lesson which we have overlooked hidden in crumbling ruins of departed civilization? Could it be that our own falling water table, dried-up springs, man-made dust bowls and abandoned cattle ranges are the early symptoms of the same blight which turned the ancient garden spots into deserts? The scientists who have read the hieroglyphics written in the sands of time say it is not a coincidence but an invariable rule. Other scientists, seeking a formula by which we may avoid such a future, have given us assurance that, taken in time, soils, vegetation and subsoil water tables can be made to persist indefinitely and yield a balanced production of life's necessities.

Fragmentary translations of ancient hieroglyphics give hints of further illuminating data on internal conditions which preceded those early tribal migrations and resultant interracial conflicts of old. They are the only hints but they tally so accurately with known cycles of modern social upheavals that they leave room for more than a suspicion that there is a standard cycle of social and economic phenomena directly associated with the disappearance of natural resources.

Boastful praise of riches and self-glorification marked the writings and arts of newly established principalities on new and virgin lands. A note of social discontent crept into the ancient records when drought and pestilence smote the flocks. (Sounds like Kansas, Arkansas and the Dakotas.) Shepherds staged a revolution which was put down by the King's Guards. Labor complained of the high price of food. Redistribution of wealth was strongly advocated as a cure for the social discontent and was tried but whether it did any temporary good or not the cycle of event went forward as per schedule and when natural resources had been pretty well used up the governments proceeded to pick a fuss with their neighbors which resulted in a war of conquest and the pressure of population on natural resources was relieved, probably only until the new pastures gave out.

Records do not disclose whether they inflated the currency, indulged in boondoggling or talked of substituting a socialized state for the existing government, but if they did it would only make more complete the parallel between disappearing natural resources 8,000 years ago and the phe nomena which have marked the social convulsions in modern times.

One of the first things that always happens when populations outgrow nature's britches is that the existing government is overthrown, usually accompanied by throat cutting and broken heads. That seems to have been standard practice down through the ages, and still is. Spain has given us a complete dramatization of this part of the cycle of social evolution during the last decade.

History of Civilization

Boiled down to the fundamentals, the history of civilization since man was created is largely made up of the rise and fall of governments, kings and empires through the exhaustion of resources. History, therefore, in reality turns out to be the story of hungry man in search of food. Conservation is the job of so managing our soils, waters and gifts of nature on this continent of ours that man's search for these necessities shall not be in vain.

If we do neglect conservation, as history has ignored it in the past, and any considerable portion of our population does search in vain for existence, we shall have increasing poverty, social upheavals and, *in spite of our high ideals and worship of peace,* we shall have *more* wars instead of *fewer,* for wars are the spawn of empty stomachs, and empty stomachs follow, as the night follows the day, the excess of demand for natural resources over the supply. Sociologists and economic doctors should study Biology.

No one can look at this continent today, compare it with the way we found it, and deny that we have ruthlessly ignored this law of Nature.

America is no richer than her remaining resources.

Hunger has, since the world began, thrown men at each other's threoats. Hunger, or the threat of it, has been and still is one of the compelling forces back of racial struggles. Comparative peace reigns in all the biological world until the competition for sustenance precipitates a death struggle. America is not exempt from this rule of Nature.

Where We Stand Today

I would like to take you aside for a moment and whisper a few confidences which might not sound so well in print. Most of the boasted conservation activities up to date are pretty badly overrated. Oh, their intentions were fine and they aimed in the right direction but they really have gotten nowhere toward the main fundamental objectives of conservation. They may sound like treason to a great cause and I'm sure those who have swallowed all the hokum about what was going to be done and assumed that therefore the intentions were accomplished facts will gasp with surprise. All right, get through gasping and then we'll go on.

The Soil Conservation Service in the Department of Agriculture is the most valuable custodian of our No. 1 precious natural resource and is headed by one of the greatest authorities on land use and sound soil management in the world. His Service was cut to the bone in appropriations and personnel three years before the threat of the present war made such a sacrifice necessary.

The U. S. Forest Service was without an authorized head, leader or Chief for about two years, while the morale in that great agency of conservation fell to the lowest ebb in 25 years.

The Fish and Wildlife Service (formerly the Bureau of Biological Survey and U. S. Bureau of Fisheries) under as sturdy and able a conservation leader as lives, has been so crippled by cuts in its personnel and appropriations that maintenance of many of its restoration and refuge projects will have to be curtailed.

Economy? God bless it, yes. But one-fifth of the cost of the abandoned Passamaquoddy power project or the Florida Ship Canal would be more than all these curtailed conservation agencies ever dreamed of spending in their most ambitious years. And the so-called Florida Ship Canal, condemned by every scientific authority as more damaging than beneficial, is still on the authorized project list of the Administration.

If the Florida Ship Canal was the only boondoggle to be fed cream while orthodox agencies of conservation starved, we might excuse it on the grounds that the Administration thought it was a justified project, for reasons unknown to science. But when we add to the Florida Ship Canal and Passamaquoddy fiasco, the Santee-Cooper fifty million dollar project and the two hydro-electric dams in the Columbia River which cost more than the Panama Canal and killed more salmon than can be bought with all the electricity the two dams can make, the score against the Administration's espousal of conservation collapses like your rear tire after a blow-out. While these boondogglers were lapping up hundreds of millions like ice cream at a Sunday School picnic, the Administration kept its foot against the door whenever a conservation agency called. I should know, for I was Chief of the Biological Survey then.

And where was the great voice of the aroused conservation-minded public all this time? There wasn't any voice and there wasn't any aroused conservation-minded public. The reason is simple enough. The great American public had grown up under an educational system which taught that America could feed the world; that our natural resources were inexhaustible and why Hannibal crossed the Alps, but not one hint as to the future which awaited a nation depleted of its natural resources. That public has been buying sweetened water at a dollar a bottle with a conservation label on it ever since, and doesn't yet know the difference.

The Governors of most states are totally ignorant of the fundamental principles of natural resource conservation and think that biological management means some kind of birth control. When we do find a state executive who is a convert to the cause, he finds that there aren't enough technically qualified conservationists in the state to form a good Conservation Commission. You will understand, of course, that in speaking of conservationists I am not talking about a shortage of sportsmen and their particular branch of wildlife conservation, nor of bird lovers nor wild flower fans. While they have done more than anyone else and paid all the bills up to date, few of them understand that you can't restock a barren lake or stream with fish until you have restored the balanced chemistry of the waters, any more than you can repopulate the Kansas Dust Bowl by running landseekers' excursions to it. Too many bird lovers look at their bird feeding trays with pride of accomplishment, unaware that a feeding tray is nothing more than a "relief soup kitchen" in a national ornithological depression. A bird in a bush is worth two on a feeding tray. Many states have passed laws prohibiting the picking of wild flowers, apparently unaware that it wasn't so much picking the wild flowers that destroyed them as it was the devastation of the environment necessary for their propagation.

In conclusion let me say that I have shared the hopes, the enthusiasms and the disappointments with each one of these divergent efforts to achieve conservation objectives. Every type of Federal and State conservation administration has been tried, with indifferent success. Voluntary organizations which sought to unite the conservationists into powerful nation-wide movements have failed dismally. Conservation magazines and conservation evangelists have broadcast the message from coast to coast but destructive exploitation still rules the land. Conservation is a sissy with ruffled pantalettes, a May basket in her hand and a yellow ribbon in her hair.

Education in Conservation—the Only Real Road to Success

After all these years of effort to find some formula of conservation which would work I am convinced that until a new generation is taught in the Public Schools man's utter dependence on natural resources, until the teachers of Botany, Chemistry, Biology and Geology emphasize the functions rather than the terminology of their respective sciences; until in fact we have a majority of the American public schooled in the fundamental principles of conservation, criminal waste will continue to reduce our heritage of natural resources. If you will begin to work soon on the youth now in the grade schools, it will not be too awfully late.

To me, Education has become the only pathway that can lead us out of the doldrums.

The Conservation Commentator of "Science News Letter," Dr. Frank Thone, recently summed up the conservation situation about as follows: Failure to practice the principles of conservation is largely due to the failure of our educational institutions to teach conservation, and the reason for this deficiency is that teachers have not been taught how to teach conservation.

A prominent educator of wide experience recently told me that there was one great unsolved problem in pedagogy. Teachers graduated from the best Teachers' Colleges continued to go forth and teach their pupils what they had been taught by their Public School teachers. They might use the new methods of progressive education but what they passed on to the students were the concepts they had acquired in their own earlier years in school.

Thus teachers were still continuing to teach what their teachers had taught, who in turn taught what their teachers had taught them. If this be true it is only a deadly parallel to the mental habits of our whole adult population who continue to the grave living by the convictions implanted in their minds when the North American continent was new and its riches undespoiled. It constitutes a major challenge to the educators. The battle for conservation seems to me to present many aspects similar to the recent battle of little nations of Europe against the organized Axis predators. We can all see now that if the small free nations had banded together to fight the invader instead of succumbing to Hitler's "divide and conquer" strategy the story of the first years of the war would have been a different one and victory not so long delayed.

In the battle for conservation we have as many organized subdivisions, each working along, as there were little nations in Europe. It was with the hope of uniting these subdivisions and coordinating their combined efforts against the wasting of resources that the National Wildlife Federation was proposed and its organization attempted. Some such device for unification seems desirable in the extreme needs of the years to come. Whether or not it succeeds depends on the willingness of the public to give the matter their attention.